SRA OpenCourt Reading

Bizz Buzz

A Division of The McGraw·Hill Companies

Columbus, Ohio

MW00891088

www.sra4kids.com

SRA/McGraw-Hill

A Division of The **McGraw·Hill** *Companies*

Send all inquiries to:
SRA/McGraw-Hill
8787 Orion Place
Columbus, OH 43240-4027

ISBN 0-07-569460-3
  2 3 4 5 6 7 8 9 DBH 05 04 03 02

Is it a buzz?
It is a big buzz.

Is it a fizz?
Buzz, fizz.
What is it?

Bizz, bizz.
Buzz, fizz.
Bop! Bam!

Can it be Dad?
It is not Dad.

Yes!

It is jazz!
It is a jazz band.
A jazz band is fun!